Birthday

by Liza Charlesworth

ISBN: 978-1-338-78286-8
Illustrated by Erika Lynne Jones
Copyright © 2021 by Liza Charlesworth. All rights reserved.
Published by Scholastic Inc., 557 Broadway, New York, NY 10012

10 9 8 7 6 5 4 3 2 1   68   21 22 23 24 25 26 27/0

Printed in Jiaxing, China. First printing, June 2021.

Which animal has a balloon?
Cat has that!

Which animal has a hat?
Pig has that!

3

Which animal has a horn?
Fox has that!

FOR YOU

Which animal has a present?
Dog has that!

5

Which animal has a cake?
Turtle has that!

Shhhhhhhhhhhhhhhhhhhh!

Which animal has a surprise?
Bear has that!